MW00581913

PAMELA R. WEISS

WITH ILLUSTRATIONS BY
ALLI FISHER

your WORLD

A BOOK OF COMFORT

*for parents, teachers
and caregivers*

TO BENEFIT KIDS OF ALL AGES

Dear Reader,

You are about to embark on a very different kind of reading journey. *Your World* begins with and depicts a loving attachment between parent and child. And (good news!) it ends just as it begins.

This is, indeed, an illustrated text for children and can be considered a children's book, and yet ~ there is more to it.

To Our World's Beautiful Children and Teens: I hope that when you turn these pages that you feel cared for and held. Internalize these words. Always know how much you matter.

To Courageous Parents and Caregivers: When you turn these pages, allow yourself to see how massive a role you play in your child's life. You are your children's number one influencers. These words are for you more than anyone.

To Courageous Teachers: As you read these words, see how big your role is as well. Your role is larger than life, with so many curious eyes watching your every move. By all means, use *Your World* gently as a learning tool.

To Each Individual: Allow this book to be a source of calm and comfort. Allow it to remind you that you have what it takes to be there for yourself.

To each of us whether or not anchored to another: Allow *Your World* to bring your many internal parts toward self understanding and an abundance of affirmations.

May *Your World* remind you that we also have the privilege and the right to depend, yes to depend, on one another. We all need each other.

Lastly, as for the historic events noted, please feel free to insert events in history or current events that speak to you, so as to make this book, all the more so, your very own.

Pamela R. Weissman
July 10, 2023

When you were born,
you were held close.

We rocked and cuddled together.

We played a lot ~ a whole bunch!

We played with dolls and trucks and blocks, and we colored, and …

Well, what didn't we play together, if you think about it?

We laughed a whole bunch, too!

I see you getting bigger every day!

Look at you now, as you are becoming one who can walk and waddle, one who can talk and toddle.

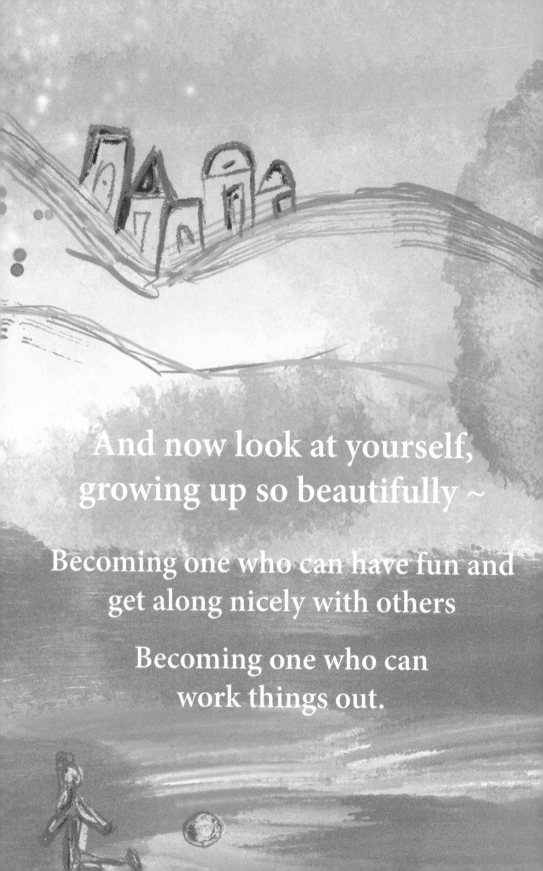

And now look at yourself,
growing up so beautifully ~

Becoming one who can have fun and
get along nicely with others

Becoming one who can
work things out.

I love to cheer you on!
Go you!

I continue to hold you
close, with all the love in
my heart,

here by your side.

And, with each passing day,
you begin to learn.

Yes, to learn
and to discover

Reading!

Math!

The Arts!

Written
Expression!

Science!

Sports!

As you grow up, you begin to discover the world's stories.

Remarkable

stories

about ...

Inventions!

Explorations!

Aviations!

Industrializations!

Declarations!

Freedoms!

As you grow up, you
begin to notice the
beauty and bounty

of our natural world.

But, my dear child,

sometimes in our world at large and in our own little universe, things can go wrong.

It is not always easy
to understand, so we will hold
hands and take a look together.

Before you are three days
etched in time.

They are moments of
commemoration from
which to learn

from which
to grow.

Martin Luther King Jr. Day

commemorates the birthday of a great civil rights leader. This is a day of very raw pain. MLK Jr. was a staunch advocate for Black Americans and all people of color.

As we shed tears of deep sorrow and try to understand why Martin Luther King Jr. was assassinated, let us promise to never forget his profound words and his powerful messages:

To genuinely respect diversity

To care for the underserved

And to celebrate each individual's unique humanity

On the last Monday in May, we find ourselves plagued by the losses of war as we observe Memorial Day.

Be it Memorial Day or Remembrance Day ...

We remember those who lost their lives in combat, and we salute our veterans.

They and their families are our heroes.

While conveying our respect,
may we always recall

Their selfless sacrifice

Their incomparable courage

Their abiding loyalty

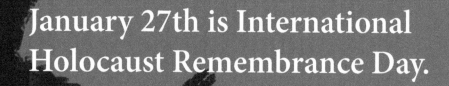

January 27th is International
Holocaust Remembrance Day.

On this day, we mourn the loss of
millions of innocent lives, including
Jews and countless other minorities.
This is the period in history where
we find ourselves grappling, trying to
make some sense of this reality.

And yet, here we stand ~

Bearing witness to indomitable
human strength

Bearing witness to unparalleled
perseverance

Bearing witness to the tenderness and
compassion from those who risked
their lives to help save others

So

how

do

we

make

sense

of

it

all

?

How?

We may not be able
to change what has so
sadly occurred

or understand the
challenges of today.

Let's pause and try to remember the following, as *this is my answer:*

As you learn of these challenging parts of history,

and as you contend and
wrestle with your own unique
sets of challenges,

I am here.

I am here to listen to
how you are affected
by any and all of it.

Whether we are in close
proximity or live at a distance
or even if only in your
imagination, I am
holding you.

You are held.

Allow yourself to feel reassured.

Allow yourself to remember when we rocked and cuddled.

Allow yourself to recall the security we created when we laughed and played together.

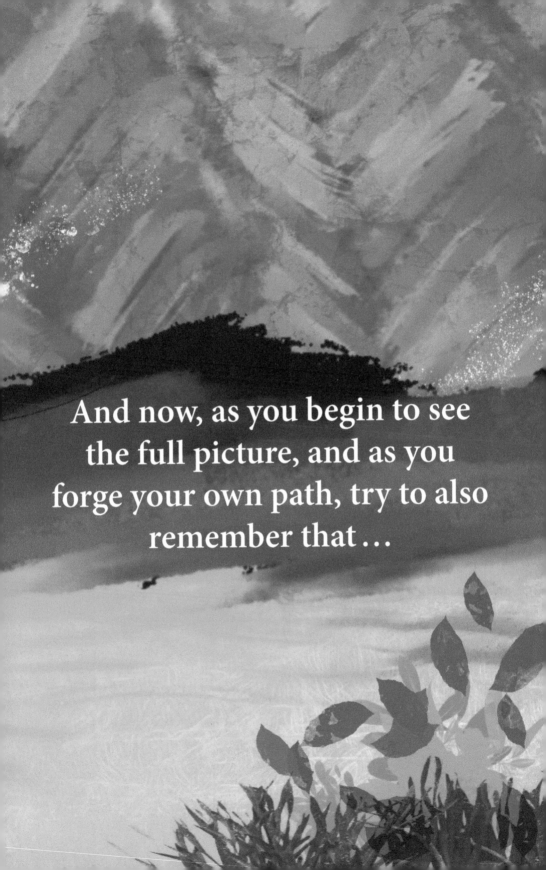

And now, as you begin to see the full picture, and as you forge your own path, try to also remember that…

At times in the world there may be PREJUDICE.

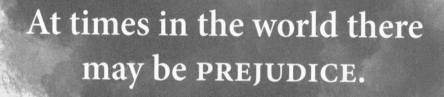

In your world may there be *acceptance.*

And at times there may
be PUSHINESS.

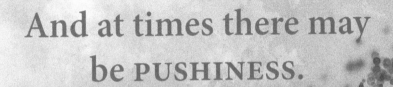

In your world may there be
humility.

There may be INEQUITIES but in
your world may there always be

enough.

There may be CALLOUSNESS.
May yours become one of

compassion.

There may be VIOLENCE & STRIFE.
In your world may there be

*healthy assertion &
respectful disagreement.*

In the world there may be UNREST.
May yours be filled with

stability.

And there may be IMPATIENCE.

In your world may there be
understanding & *humor.*

In the world there
may be CONFLICT.
In yours may there be …

peace of mind.

So go live and learn just
as the day you were born ~
held and *loved*.

For the ones I love who make my world the joy that it is:

For Neil, my one and only

For my children, sweet masterpieces—loved and forever held

For their spectacular life partners (in-loves),

and

For my precious grandchildren—
You are all my world!

—PAMELA R. WEISSMAN

To the ones I deeply love who brighten my world:

For my incredible Parents—Supportive souls, who inspire
and care, always.

For my treasured Grandparents,
Teachers and Friends—Thank you all for always holding
me with so much love.

To all my Students—May you continue to light up the
world and know you are always held.

—ALLI FISHER

PAMELA R. WEISSMAN

is a Social Worker in private practice in Baltimore, Maryland. Pam specializes in individual, group and family therapy, with a concentration on grief and trauma-informed care. Pam has worked in education as a teacher and as a School Social Worker and when she is not writing, reading, cooking, dancing with her family in her kitchen or enjoying the company of family and friends, she is teaching at least three Latin/Zumba dancing classes each week. Visit her at PAMELAWEISSMAN.COM

ALLI FISHER

is the Creative Arts director and founder of Woven Dreams, which focuses on Choice-Based art education. She is a graduate of Towson University and visiting student of Gallaudet University where she holds a dual degree in Art and Design, with a focus in Education, and Deaf Studies. Living in Jerusalem, Alli teaches her students, online and in person, to thrive as artists through creative self expression. Visit her at WOVEN-DREAMS.COM.

First published by BRAI Publications in 2023

ISBN: 978-1-7359821-0-6 (hardcover)

BRAI Publications is named in honor of
Bashe, Royal, Alice and Irving: parents for the ages.

Book design by Pamela R. Weissman,
Alli Fisher, and Adam Robinson.

For inquiries, bulk purchases, and engagements,
visit PAMELAWEISSMAN.COM

Printed in the USA
CPSIA information can be obtained
at www.ICGtesting.com
LVHW051652100923
757619LV00017B/272/J